# Contents

# Carnival time for Joshua

Every day Joshua's dad came home from work, had his tea and then went off to play music on the steel drums with his band.

"Soon it will be the carnival," he said to Joshua. "It will be great fun. I hope our team will win the competition for the best costumes and the best steel band."

Joshua's mum and granny were making carnival costumes for all the family. This year, the carnival team from their street were going as birds, with lovely red, yellow and green feathers on their costumes. Joshua helped to stick the feathers and gold buttons on to the costumes. It was very hard because everything was so sticky.

When he got into a mess, Granny helped him to sort out the feathers. She couldn't see, but she had very clever fingers.

At last it was the day of the carnival. Everyone got up early and put on their costumes.

"You look great, Dad!" said Joshua. Dad was dressed in a purple suit with a big black and white hat. "Mum's feathers look beautiful, too."

"Come on, Joshua," said Mum. "It's time to put your costume on now."

Joshua had a blue and white costume, even though he wasn't going to walk in the carnival parade. He was going to sit with Granny and watch the parade go by and tell her about all the exciting things he could see.

"Now, Granny, look after Joshua," said Dad.

"And Joshua, you look after Granny," said Mum. "We've got to go and meet our team now. You sit up there and watch."

Joshua and Granny sat high above the crowd. It was very noisy and exciting. The crowd waved flags and blew whistles. Lots of balloons floated up in the sky and a helicopter was flying above.

Soon, the lorries came slowly along the street. There were steel bands playing exciting music and lots of people walking and dancing in their carnival costumes.

"There are some people dressed as crocodiles and elephants, Granny!" shouted Joshua. "And here's a lorry with a great big cake on the back! All the people are sitting on the cake! Now here comes one like a boat!"

"Can you see our bird team yet?" asked Granny.

"No, not yet," said Joshua.

At last, the bird team came along.

"Here they are!" cried Joshua. "Dad's on the lorry playing with the band and I can see Mum dancing with all the others! They look great!"

It was very exciting. Joshua jumped down and ran through the crowd and waved to Mum and Dad. But Mum and Dad didn't see him, and the lorry kept going along the road. Soon it was out of sight.

Joshua turned round. Where was Granny? He couldn't see her anywhere in the crowd. All he could see were people's legs. He was lost! Joshua started to shout for Granny, but he still couldn't find her.

"Hello, Joshua," said Mrs Green. She lived in Joshua's street. "Can I help?"

"I've lost my Granny in the crowd," said Joshua.

"Then we must ask all these people to help us to find her," said Mrs Green.

She lifted Joshua up so he could see over the crowd.

"My friend Joshua has lost his Granny," she called to the crowd. "Can you see her anywhere?"

Everyone shouted, "Joshua's Granny, where are you?"

Soon, Granny shouted from the back of the crowd, "Here I am!"

"Here she is!" shouted all the people. So Mrs Green passed Joshua to the next person, who passed him to the next one, over the top of the crowd. Joshua started to laugh. This was fun!

Soon he was back with Granny. They waved and shouted thank you to the crowd and went to meet Mum and Dad.

Mum and Dad had some good news! They had won the competition for the best costumes and the best steel band! Everyone was very happy. They went and danced with the crowd until it went dark.

At the end of the carnival there were fireworks which made blue and red and yellow stars across the black sky.

"Aren't they beautiful!" said Mum.

"Just like our costumes!" said Joshua.

# The Christmas tree

Have you seen the Christmas tree

    Christmas tree

    Christmas tree –

Have you seen the Christmas tree

    That's hung with silver light?

I can tell you where it's been,
  Where it's been
  Hardly seen
Crowded in the forest green
  And shadowed out of sight...

Now it's shiny, let us sing –
  Let us sing
  Carolling!
Look... it's jewelled like a king
  For everyone's delight!

*Jean Kenward*

# Pancake day

"Today is pancake day, children," said Mrs Dale. "Mr Jones has put the flags up in the village hall ready for the pancake festival tonight."

The children had made lots of red, blue and green flags to decorate the village hall.

"Who is going to make the pancakes for the pancake tossing competition?" asked Paul.

"We are!" said Mrs Dale. "We're going to do it this afternoon." Everyone looked very excited.

In the afternoon, the children came into the classroom and found some very interesting things on the tables. Everyone had a spoon, a bowl and some milk. In the bowl was some flour, salt and an egg.

"Don't start yet!" said Mrs Dale. "Now watch me. Mix the flour with the egg and add the milk slowly, like this. Mix it very slowly. This is called pancake batter. Now you can start when you're ready."

So everyone started. What a mess! Jimmy had some trouble with his batter. It was too thick, so Mrs Dale helped him. Then Alice started crying because she got some flour on her clothes. Sam dropped his spoon and got batter all over the floor.

At last everyone had finished and Mrs Dale helped them to pour the batter into a big bowl.

"All right," she said. "I'm going to show you how to toss the pancakes now, ready for the pancake tossing competition tonight."

She took them into the small school kitchen.

"Now keep back while I cook a pancake," said
Mrs Dale. She poured some oil into a frying pan and put
in some batter. She cooked it for a little while.

"Watch this," she said. "You have to toss it as high as
you can and catch it in the frying pan."

She tossed the pancake very high and caught it in the
pan. Everyone cheered.

"That's what you're going to do tonight," she said.

"I can't wait!" said Paul.

At last it was time to go to the village hall for the competition.

"Look, Mum," said Jimmy. "We made those flags at school."

"They look great," said Mum.

"There's Sam's mum, cooking our batter," shouted Alice. All the children watched while she cooked one side and then tossed the pancake and cooked the other side.

"Hello, everybody," shouted the vicar. "Thank you to all the children for making the lovely flags and the pancake batter. We will start outside with the pancake race for the older children."

18

The children got ready with their frying pans and pancakes.

"Ready, steady, GO!" shouted Mrs Dale.

They started to run. They had to race round the village green, tossing pancakes at the same time. It was great fun. Some of the children tossed the pancakes too high and couldn't catch them. Sam's big sister nearly won, but then she fell over in the grass.

"Hooray!" cheered Alice as her brother got back to the village hall first.

"Well done!" said Mrs Dale. "Now it's time for my
class to do the pancake tossing competition. The person
who can toss the pancake the highest will win. But
remember, you must catch it in your frying pan as well!"

All the mums and dads stood watching. Jimmy's dog,
Scruff, sat at the front. The children got into a line.
One by one they tossed a pancake.

Soon, it was Jimmy's turn. As he tossed the pancake, Scruff jumped up high into the air.

"NO!" shouted Jimmy, but it was too late. Scruff caught the pancake in his mouth and began to eat it as quickly as he could. Everybody in the hall laughed and Scruff looked very happy too. Only Jimmy looked cross.

"Oh dear!" laughed the vicar. "I think you'd better have another go, Jimmy!" So Jimmy had a new pancake and Mum held on to Scruff while he had another go.

At the end of the competition, the vicar gave out
the prizes. Paul won a book for tossing his pancake
the highest. Then everyone went to the big table, where
Sam's mum gave out pancakes for everybody to eat.
At the end of the line was Scruff.

"Shall I give anything to Scruff?" asked Sam's mum.

"YES!" cheered all the children.

"Here you are," said Jimmy, and he gave Scruff the
biggest pancake of all.

# Diwali

"Guess what I've got in my bag," said Kamla in the playground.

"What?" asked Ben.

"A Diwali card," said Kamla. "A Diwali card for my mum."

"Diwali?" said Ben. "What's Diwali?"

"Oh, Diwali is a lovely festival," said Kamla.

"We don't have it in our house," said Ben.

"Never mind," said Kamla. "I think we're going to have some special Diwali things at school next week. Just wait and see."

Kamla was right.

One morning Miss Hill asked the Hindu children to help her to tell everyone about Diwali. They told the story of the great Rama and his terrible enemy Ravana. Rama and Ravana had a long battle.

"Who won the battle?" asked Miss Hill.

"Rama!" shouted the children.

"And how do we welcome him home?" she asked.

"With lights," they answered.

"Yes," said Miss Hill. "Diwali is the Hindu Festival of Light."

The children made big pictures of Rama and his enemy Ravana.

"We need ten people to paint Ravana," said Kamla. "One for each head." Then they made lanterns to go in the classroom window.

"Shall we make mendhi patterns now?" asked Miss Hill.

"Mendhi patterns?" thought Ben. "Patterns on your hand?" He watched carefully as Miss Hill mixed the powder in a bowl.

"Oh, that's good," he said. "Can I do one now for someone?"

The next day, Ben had a surprise. Kamla's mum and dad asked him to a Diwali party.

"Diwali is for everyone," they said.

Kamla's house was full of lights. Everyone wore their best party clothes. There was music and lovely food. Then, best of all, there were fireworks. Bang! Crash! Ohhh! The fireworks lit up the sky.

"That's the end of the festival of Diwali," said Kamla's dad.

"Until next time!" said Ben.

# The big tidy-up

"Dad, can I help you to tidy up the garden shed?" asked Jo, one Saturday morning. Dad looked surprised.

"It's not my birthday, is it?" he said, hiding a smile. "It's not Be-Good-To-Dad-Day, is it?"

"No, but can I?" said Jo.

"What makes you think I was going to tidy up the garden shed?" said Dad.

"It needs a tidy-up," said Jo.

It was true. There was lots of rubbish in the shed which Dad needed to throw away.

"All right," said Dad. "We can do it this morning."

"Mum, can I help you to tidy up the loft?" asked Mark, that Saturday morning. Mum looked surprised.

"It's not Mother's Day, is it?" she said, hiding a smile. "It's not Help-Dear-Old-Mum Week, is it?"

"No, don't be silly," said Mark. "But can I help?"

"The loft does need a tidy-up, it's true," said Mum. "Perhaps we could do it this morning."

"Good," said Mark. "Come on."

A few houses away, David and Mel were looking out of the kitchen window at a tree in the garden. It was a very old tree and the branches on it were very low.

"The branches on that tree need cutting," said David. "Very tall people would hit their head on them."

"We don't know any very tall people," said Dad. Mum went across to the window and looked out.

"The branches are low," she said. "Perhaps it does need cutting."

"We could help you, Dad," said Mel.

"We could pick up the branches," said David. Dad looked very surprised.

"But you don't like helping in the garden," he said.

"We do today," said Mel.

"Come on, Dad," said David.

At a shop on the estate, Neeta and Leela were helping their uncle to tidy up the back room. There was a lot of rubbish to throw out. Their uncle had been surprised when Neeta and Leela had offered to help him.

"It's very nice of you," he said.

"That's all right," said Neeta.

"We're happy to help," said Leela.

Paul was helping the school caretaker to clean out the store-room at school that Saturday morning.

"It's good of you to give me a hand, Paul," said the caretaker. "There are some broken chairs to throw away."

Paul smiled.

"I don't mind helping," he said.

Later that Saturday morning, a policeman was going through the estate on his bike. First, he saw Jo pushing some garden rubbish across the road. Then he saw Mark carrying some old things.

David and Mel were pulling bits of tree branches. Then Neeta and Leela went by with some old boxes and newspapers. Next the policeman saw Paul with some old, broken chairs. They were all going to the field at the back of the estate.

"What's going on?" thought the policeman. "I'll ride across the field and see."

When he got there, he saw... a big bonfire! The policeman laughed. "How could I forget Bonfire Night?"

On Bonfire Night, there was a very, very big bonfire.

"One good thing about Bonfire Night," laughed Jo's dad. "Everyone has a big tidy-up and for once we can get the children to help!"

# Chinese New Year

The Chinese New Year is a quiet family time in China, but in other places round the world, Chinese people celebrate the New Year for a week or more.

The children have beautiful new clothes to start the year. Everyone cleans the house, ready for the New Year, and they put up lanterns and decorate the house with flowers.

There is special food for New Year. People eat dumplings made with sugar and nuts, with a little surprise present inside. They also give sweets to their visitors.

When visitors come, they bring presents and wish each other good luck and wish that everyone will have lots of money. Sometimes, the children get red envelopes with lucky money inside. Red is the Chinese lucky colour, so people write messages on red paper and put them up all over the house.

New Year is thought to be everyone's birthday so all Chinese people are one year older on that day, even if they were born only the day or week before.

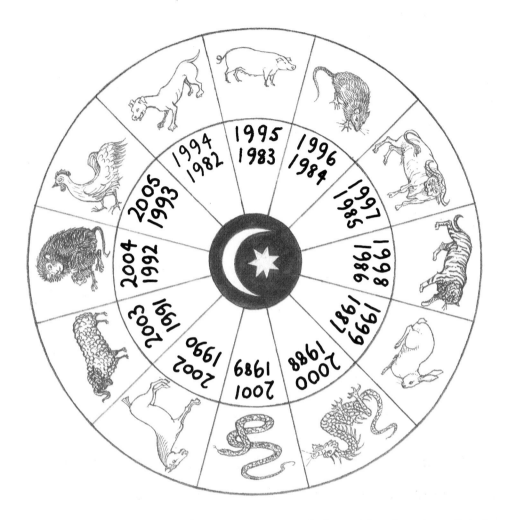

This calendar shows which animal each year is called after.

Every year, the Chinese New Year starts some time between 21st January and 19th February, on the day when there is a new moon.

Each Chinese New Year is called after one of twelve animals, in turn. The animals are rat, ox, tiger, rabbit, dragon, snake, horse, ram, monkey, cock, dog and pig.

There is an old Chinese story which says that all the
animals had a swimming race across a river to see who
should give his name to the first year of all. The clever
rat won by sitting on the back of the ox and jumping off
so he was the first on the other side.

There are Chinese New Year celebrations in most cities each year.

On Chinese New Year day, there are parades in lots of towns all over the world. Hundreds of people go to see the parade in the streets and have fun. There is a dancing lion with big round eyes and a long dragon made of brightly painted paper and cloth. People carry the dragon on their backs so you can only see their legs under the dragon costume. They make the dragon hop and jump and dance through the streets.

The lion and the dragon roar and shake their heads to frighten away any bad luck. The people in the crowd give presents of money to the people inside the dancing dragon to thank them for doing this.

When night comes there are beautiful fireworks whizzing across the sky and their bangs also frighten bad luck away.